What a Windy Day!

Written by Cynthia Rider
Illustrated by Nicola Evans

WAYLAND

What a windy day!
The wind is blowing
the leaves away.

What a windy day!
The wind is blowing
the bin away.

What a windy day!
The wind is blowing
the football away.

9

What a windy day!
The wind is blowing
the umbrella away.

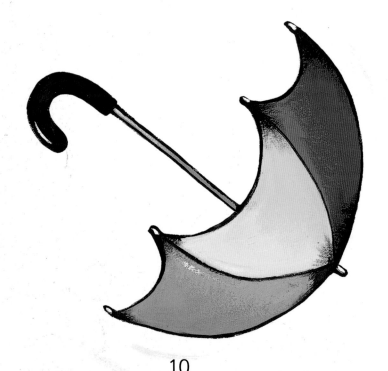

What a windy day!
The wind is blowing
the letters away.

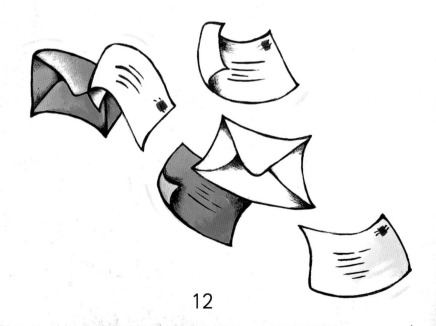

13

What a windy day!
The wind is blowing
Mum's washing away.

What a windy day!
The wind is blowing
Baby's hat away.

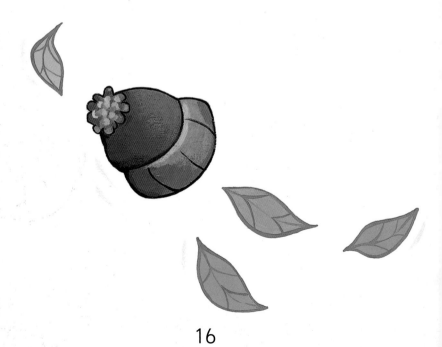

17

What a windy day!
The wind is blowing
me away!

What a windy day!

Guiding a First Read of
What a Windy Day!

It is important to talk through the book with the child before they read it alone. This prepares them for the way the story unfolds, and allows them to enjoy the pictures as you both talk naturally, using the language they will later encounter when reading. Read them the brief overview, and then follow the suggestions below:

1. Talking through the book
In this book, a boy and his sister are watching the wind blowing everything away.

The title of this book is: **What a Windy Day!**
Let's read the text on page 4.
"What a windy day! The wind is blowing the leaves away."
Now turn to page 6. "Whoosh! What a windy day! The wind is blowing the bin away."
Let's see what the wind is blowing away on the next page.

Continue through the book, guiding the discussion to fit the text as the child looks at the illustrations.

On page 14, the wind is blowing Mum's washing away. And on the next page, it's blowing Baby's hat away.
On page 18, the boy says, "The wind is blowing me away!" What a windy day!

2. A first reading of the book

Ask the child to read the book independently,
pointing carefully under each word (tracking),
while thinking about the story. Praise attempts
by the child to correct themselves, and prompt
them to use their letter knowledge, the punctuation
and check the meaning, for example:

**You are making the story sound really windy!
Did you spot the exclamation mark? Good reading.**

**Yes, it is a rubbish bin, but did your pointing fit?
Try it again. Well done — you fixed it yourself.**

**You said, "The wind is blowing the Baby's hat."
It is blowing the hat but just try it again and check
very carefully. Good. You left out 'the' this time.**

3. Follow-up activities

The high frequency words in this title are:

a   away   day   is   the

· Select a new high frequency word, and ask the child
  to find it throughout the book. Discuss the shape of
  the letters and the letter sounds.
· To memorise the word, ask the child to write it in
  the air, then write it repeatedly on a whiteboard
  or on paper, leaving a space between each attempt.

4. Encourage

· Reading the book again — with expression.
· Drawing a picture based on the story.
· Writing one or two sentences using
  the practised words.

START READING is a series of highly enjoyable books for beginner readers. **The books have been carefully graded to match the Book Bands widely used in schools.** This enables readers to be sure they choose books that match their own reading ability.

Look out for the Band colour on the book in our Start Reading logo.

The Bands are:

Pink Band 1A & 1B

Red Band 2

Yellow Band 3

Blue Band 4

Green Band 5

Orange Band 6

Turquoise Band 7

Purple Band 8

Gold Band 9

START READING books can be read independently or shared with an adult. They promote the enjoyment of reading through satisfying stories supported by fun illustrations.

Cynthia Rider lives in the Peak District of Derbyshire and often finds inspiration for her stories in the countryside around her. She particularly enjoys writing for young children and encouraging their love of reading.

Nicola Evans works as a freelance illustrator in a small village on the south coast of England, where she lives with her husband and three-year-old daughter. She loves illustrating for children, helping to bring books alive with her characters and colours.